Y0-CBB-208

Contents

1. One Basket of Food

The dusty road disappeared over the hills to the south toward Jerusalem. Jewish pilgrims were traveling to Jerusalem for the Passover festival. They could hardly wait to get there!

But something interrupted their journey. And it all centered around a boy with some food. Just who was this boy? And where did the food come from?

Perhaps his name was Aram, and perhaps it all began like this:

"It's always the same," Aram grumbled to himself. Every year he sat by the road selling loaves of bread and small pickled fish to the hungry travelers. Aram wished he could go too.

"But, Mother," he had begged earlier. Lots of my friends are going. And I never get to go anywhere or do anything that's exciting."

"No, Son," she said. "Someday when you are

grown you can make the journey from Galilee to Jerusalem. As for excitement, you'll have to find it around here for now."

As noon approached, Aram stood up beside his basket and began shouting, "Bread for sale! Fish for sale!" One by one the loaves and fish were sold to the hungry travelers. The wheat bread always sold the best, but wheat was expensive and Aram's mother couldn't afford to make too many wheat loaves. She made most of her bread with cheap, coarse barley flour.

When the lunch hour had passed, Aram counted the coins he had received and carefully placed them in a leather bag. "Mother will be pleased," he thought, looking into the basket of food. "I sold everything except five barley loaves and two fish."

He closed up the basket, but before he headed home for the day, he stood in the road for a little while staring south. Aram wondered what the mighty city of Jerusalem was like, and wished that someday he'd get to visit that exciting place. Suddenly he saw a cloud of dust rising over the hills.

"Looks like a troop of Roman soldiers are headed this way," he said to himself. Aram decided to stick around to watch them pass. At least that was

Who is Jesus?

By KATHLEEN M. ZAFFORE

Illustrated by NORMAN SEARS

ACCENT PUBLICATIONS
DENVER

Accent Publications, Inc.
12100 W. Sixth Avenue
P. O. Box 15337
Denver, Colorado 80215

Copyright ©1983, Revised 1984, Accent Publications, Inc.
Printed in the United States of America

ISBN 0-89636-117-9

better than nothing. But as he waited, he was surprised to see hundreds of pilgrims coming back! And they were in a big hurry!

"What's going on?" Aram shouted.

"The teacher called Jesus is rowing north on the Sea of Galilee!" one man answered. "We're going to meet Him."

Jesus! Aram had heard about this teacher, how He healed sick people and made crippled people walk again—just by His words. "If I can't go to Jerusalem, at least I can go to see Jesus!"

He tied the basket of bread onto his back and joined the parade of people.

Soon Aram could look down a grassy hill toward the sea. He could see men around a boat on the shore, and he wondered if one of them was Jesus.

"By the time I get down there, thousands of people will be around the Teacher," he said to himself sadly. "I won't even be close enough to see His face. Nothing exciting ever happens to me!"

* * * * * *

"Look at all of these people!" Peter said, surveying the crowd. "There must be 5,000 men, plus all their wives and kids!"

"We can't go anywhere anymore for peace and

quiet," Philip complained. "The crowds always find us."

"They are like a flock of sheep without a shepherd to take care of them," Jesus said lovingly.

"Master!" one man called. "Heal my illness!" And many people in the crowd joined in asking to be healed. Jesus was tired and had been looking forward to resting with His disciples. But how could He ignore these people who needed Him?

Jesus reached out and touched the sick man gently. His illness disappeared! The people nearby cheered and pushed to get closer to the Healer.

Aram stood at the edge of the crowd. He could see the people clustering around someone far away on the hillside. "That must be Jesus," he thought. "I was right. I'll never get close enough to see Him. Oh well. Just being in this crowd is more exciting than sitting by the road selling bread."

Aram shifted the basket of food to make it more comfortable. He looked down toward the sea and saw the little boat on the beach. He had never been in a boat, so he decided to take a closer look.

"Hello," Aram said to the man by the boat. "Did

you come with the Teacher?"

"I sure did," Andrew said with a smile. "Have you gotten to see the Teacher?"

"No," said Aram. "He's too far away and there are too many people around Him." The boy looked into the boat curiously.

"Would you like to sit in the boat?" Andrew asked.

"Sure!" Aram said excitedly.

"I'll hold your basket for you," Andrew said. "What's in it?"

"Oh, just five loaves of barley bread and two pickled fish. They're left over from what I was selling to the Passover pilgrims," Aram said, hopping into the boat.

Just then, the shouts of the crowd grew louder. Aram shielded his eyes against the late afternoon sun and saw Jesus heading down the hill toward the beach!

"You may get to see the Teacher after all," Andrew said.

Jesus looked at all of the people gathered on the hillside. The nearest village was several miles away and it was getting close to dinner time.

Jesus called his disciples over to Him. Andrew was still holding Aram's basket of food.

"Come on," Andrew said. Aram leaped out of the boat and tagged along. He saw Jesus standing in the center of a group of men. Aram couldn't believe how close he was to the Teacher. This was getting more exciting by the minute!

Jesus turned to His disciple, Philip. "How are we going to feed all of these people?" He asked. Jesus already knew what He would do, but He wondered how Philip would solve the problem.

"We have some money in our treasury box," Philip answered. "But it's not enough to buy bread to feed this crowd!"

Jesus looked around at the other disciples. Aram tugged at Andrew's shirt and pointed to his basket.

"This boy has five loaves of barley bread and two fish that he is willing to give to us," Andrew said. Jesus smiled at Aram and took the basket. "It won't go very far in this crowd," Andrew added.

Aram loved the look on Jesus' strong face. He could tell that something really exciting was about to happen.

"Get all of the people organized into groups and make them sit down," Jesus said. The twelve men quickly carried out the order.

Jesus reached into Aram's basket and pulled out

the loaves and fish. "Thank you, Father," He prayed. "You provide what we need every day. Amen." He broke the bread, divided the fish, and gave the pieces to the disciples. "Pass out food to everyone," He said.

The disciples didn't question Jesus. They walked through the crowd and gave everyone something to eat. When everyone had eaten enough, Jesus sent the disciples around to collect the leftovers. There were enough pieces of bread and fish left over to fill twelve baskets!

"This man is God's prophet!" the people on the hillside shouted. "Let's make Him King!"

Aram shouted too. "Jesus should be the King!" The boy couldn't imagine a better man for the job. He would never forget the love that he had seen in the Teacher's eyes.

Aram turned to look at Jesus again, but He was gone. Jesus had slipped away quietly to be by Himself to pray. It wasn't time for Him to become the King yet.

Aram was sorry that he couldn't see Jesus one last time before he headed home across the dark hills. "I'm glad we didn't go to Jerusalem," he thought happily. "Seeing Jesus has been the most exciting thing that could've happened to me!"

2. One Windy Night

When the sun had finally set, the crowd of people on the hillside began to leave to find campsites or inns where they could spend the night. The disciples gathered by the small boat.

"Get in, everyone," Peter ordered. "Jesus said He'd meet us back in Capernaum. Let's get going before the wind gets too strong."

The disciples hopped in the little boat. Six of the men grabbed oars and started rowing through the choppy water. The wind grew stronger, driving the water into large, forceful waves that knocked at the bow of the boat.

Story based on Matthew 14:22-33

"It'll take all night to get to Capernaum with this wind blowing against us," Andrew shouted. "You who aren't rowing now had better try to get some rest so you can take over for us later on tonight."

They all agreed, and six men curled up on the damp floor of the boat. The wind blew all night and the waves crashed against the hull. Just before three, the rowers awakened the sleeping disciples.

"Your turn!" Philip called.

Peter stretched his legs and stared out into the dark, windy night looking for landmarks on shore. "We haven't gone very far, have we?" he asked.

"For every mile we row, we get blown back two," Philip said wearily. "If this wind doesn't stop soon, Jesus will beat us to Capernaum. And He's walking!"

Meanwhile, Jesus stood on the shore watching the distant boat being beaten by the wind and waves. It seemed to stand still in the water. He had been on the hillside praying, and now it was time for Him to start His walk to Capernaum. But He didn't plan to take the highway. He walked straight toward the boat—on top of the water!

Peter sat in the rear of the boat, rowing steadily

and yawning sleepily. Cold sea spray blew into his face. "Brr! That'll wake me up fast!" he said to himself.

He looked around at the tall waves. To his surprise, he saw something out on the stormy water. He shook his head sharply to make sure that he was awake, because what he saw was a person—walking on the water!

The others saw it too. They jumped to their feet, their hearts pounding. The men rubbed their eyes and stared out at the high waves.

"It must be a ghost!" they yelled fearfully, and ducked down to hide.

"Don't be afraid," the "ghost" called out. "It's me, Jesus!" The disciples recognized His voice, and peeked over the edge of the boat.

"If it really is You, Lord, tell me to come out to You on the water," Peter said.

"Come to me," Jesus answered.

Peter swung his legs over the edge of the boat. The other disciples watched with their mouths hanging open. Peter began to walk across the waves toward Jesus. But then Peter looked at the mountainous waves all around him.

"Oh, no!" he screamed, suddenly afraid. Down, down he sank into the cold, dark water. "Save me,

Lord!" he called out.

Jesus grabbed the sinking man's hand and pulled him to the boat. "Your belief in me is so small," He told Peter as He lifted the soaking wet disciple into the boat.

"Lord!" John greeted Jesus happily. "Are we glad to see You! We thought we'd never get to the land because of the wind." But as he spoke, John realized that the wind had suddenly stopped. Jesus even had power over the water and the wind!

The disciples gladly went back to work rowing the boat across the calm lake.

3. The Bread of Life

As the dawning sun brightened the sky, the little boat scraped up onto the rocky beach near Capernaum. Peter and Andrew leaped out and tied the boat to a boulder. Jesus stepped over the side into the shallow muddy water and waded to the beach. The other disciples quickly followed.

"It's always good to get back to land after a stormy trip on the lake!" Andrew said.

12   Story based on John 6:22-71

"I'm starving," said Peter. "What's for breakfast?"

The disciples gathered around Jesus. He thanked God for providing food and they divided up some of the leftover barley bread and fish.

Peter stared out at the lake as he ate. He shielded his eyes against the bright morning light. Several fishing boats were headed directly toward them.

"Hello!" a voice called out. "Are you the disciples of the Teacher called Jesus?"

Peter and John stood up and waved. "We are!" John shouted back. "Who are you?"

"We are people from the crowd on the hillside," the man answered. "We looked for Jesus this morning, but we couldn't find Him. We hired these boats to bring us to Capernaum because we knew He was coming back here."

By now the boats were landing on the beach.

"Look!" another man shouted. "Jesus is already here. We've found Him!" The crowd of people jumped out of the boats and surrounded Jesus.

"How did You get here so fast, Teacher?" the man asked. "We saw Your disciples leave in the boat, but You weren't with them."

Peter smiled proudly. He was happy Jesus was popular with the people. He turned toward Jesus and was surprised at how serious his Master was.

"You aren't looking for me because of the sign you saw yesterday, but because you got your stomachs filled with bread," Jesus said. "Don't be so interested in getting bread that rots away. Look for the bread that lasts forever. I can give that bread to you."

"What do we have to do to get this lasting bread?" the people asked.

"Believe in me," Jesus said. "I was sent by God."

"If you were really sent by God, show us a sign!" the people demanded. Peter and the other disciples looked at each other with surprise. After all, Jesus had fed more than 5,000 people yesterday with only a few loaves and a couple of fish. Wasn't that a good enough sign?

God is offering to give you the true bread from Heaven. It will give life to the world," Jesus said.

"Let us have this special bread!" the people cheered, pushing closer to Jesus.

But Jesus didn't give them anything. He quietly walked toward Capernaum. John and Peter and the other disciples joined the crowd that was following.

Capernaum was always a busy city. Even the synagogue was a busy place. And that's where Jesus was headed. He knew He would find men at the synagogue who had spent their lives studying the old Scriptures and waiting for the Messiah.

"Welcome, Sir," the men said to Jesus. They knew that Jesus had healed the sick, and they had already heard how He had fed the people.

The synagogue was packed. Everyone wanted to hear Jesus. Peter squeezed through the crowd a little way, but he was forced to stand in the back of the room. He watched as Jesus stood and looked carefully at each person.

"You asked me before how to get the bread from Heaven that gives life," Jesus said. "I am the Bread of Life that I was telling you about. If you come to me you won't ever be hungry again for the things of this world that rot away. You will have eternal life if you believe in me."

Peter's mouth fell open. Jesus was claiming to be the Messiah! People all around the room understood Him and they squirmed nervously.

"How can this man be the Messiah?" Peter heard them whispering to each other. "How can He say that He came from Heaven? We know His parents—Joseph the carpenter and Mary over in the town of Nazareth."

"Stop your whispering!" Jesus ordered. "If you take the living bread once, you'll live forever!"

"That's too hard to believe," the people complained. Jesus left the synagogue. A big crowd had followed Him in, but now very few followed Him out.

The twelve men whom Jesus had chosen encircled Him. "Will you leave me, too?" He asked.

"Who else could we follow, Lord?" asked Peter. "You are the only One who promises us eternal life."

Jesus nodded sadly and said, "And yet, one of you is going to turn against me."

The little band of men slowly walked out of Capernaum. No one looked back.

4. Peter Speaks Twice

Jesus and the disciples were traveling along the hilly coast near Mount Hermon. The fresh air settled comfortably around them. The town of Caesarea Philippi was just ahead. It gleamed in the hot afternoon sun.

Each new place promised new adventure for the disciples. They had already seen many wonders since they had joined Jesus. Each disciple should have been very thankful that Jesus had chosen him.

The band of men trekked down the tree-lined road toward town. Perhaps Jesus or one of the disciples knew someone in town they could stay with. Or more likely, Jesus selected a campsite—perhaps in a little grove of trees near a bubbling brook—where the tired men could rest from their long journey.

Perhaps it was on a night just like this, when the men were resting around a campfire, when Jesus asked, "Who do men say that I am?"

The disciples glanced at each other. "I've heard some people say that You are John the Baptist," Andrew reported.

"And some say that You are Elijah," John said.

"Most people say that You are a mighty prophet of God," James said.

"Who do all of you think I am?" Jesus asked quietly. The disciples thought for awhile.

Peter straightened up, and looked right into Jesus' eyes. "You are the Son of God, the Christ," he said.

Jesus placed His hand on Peter's shoulder. "You are blessed, Peter, because my Father in Heaven is the only One who could have shown you who I really am."

Peter was filled with joy. It was wonderful to sit in the grove of trees with Jesus, the Messiah of Israel. He hoped that he would be able to be with Jesus for a long time to come.

"I will build my church," Jesus said. "Death will have no power over it. But don't tell anyone about this conversation yet."

Jesus and the disciples camped near Caesarea Philippi several days, but Jesus didn't go around healing the sick or teaching the crowds. Instead, He stayed with the twelve disciples and told them about His crucifixion and resurrection.

"Soon I must go to Jerusalem," He told them. "Many bad things will happen. In fact, I will be killed, but on the third day I will rise up from death."

Peter couldn't believe his ears! God's own Son, killed? "Teacher, I've got to talk to You for a minute," he said, pulling Jesus away from the others. "I'm worried about what You've told us about dying," Peter whispered to Jesus. "God just can't allow that to happen!"

"Get in back of me, Satan!" Jesus sharply scolded Peter. "You're just trying to keep me from doing what I must do. You aren't seeing God's plan, but only what you want to happen."

Peter looked down at the ground. He was ashamed of himself for trying to interfere with God's plan. The other disciples heard Jesus scold Peter, and they all looked over at the Teacher.

"If you are going to follow me, you will have to put your own plans aside," Jesus said. "You may even have to lose your lives because of me. But what good is it if you save your own lives now, but lose eternal life?"

The disciples didn't understand everything Jesus told them. But they still wanted to follow Him. Even if they had to die.

5. The Cloud on the Mountain

The campsite on the side of Mount Hermon was a peaceful place. There were shady orchards all around. Jesus and the twelve disciples had been there for six days. And the best part of every day was the time when they gathered around to listen to Jesus.

Jesus was glad to see the disciples getting some rest because He knew how hard the next months would be for all of them.

Peter and John gathered wood for the night's fire. "The kingdom of God that Jesus has told us about sounds great!" Peter said. "Everything will be very different when Jesus is King. The Romans won't control us anymore!"

"It does sound good," John said. "But some of the things Jesus told us bother me."

"I know," Peter agreed. "But our job is to follow Him."

As the two men stacked the wood, Jesus walked up with James. "I'm going to hike up Mount Hermon to pray," Jesus told the men. "I'd like you three to come with me." Jesus didn't have to ask twice. Peter, James, and John jumped at the chance to spend some time with Jesus.

The four men walked silently up the side of the mountain. They passed through pear orchards and fragrant groves of cedar. Finally, Jesus stopped.

They knelt down in the grass and began to pray. The sun set and the night grew darker on the mountain.

Peter yawned quietly. He loved being with Jesus, but the climb up the steep mountain had made him so sleepy. He settled back on the grass and tried again to pray. John and James glanced over at Peter. He wasn't snoring yet, but they knew he was asleep. John and James also lay back on the grass. The stars were beginning to twinkle. John thought he'd just rest his eyes for a few moments. Pretty soon he was fast asleep, and so was James.

* * * * *

Peter didn't know how long he had been sleeping, but from the brightness, he figured that the sun had already come up. He sleepily opened his eyes a crack, but the light was so bright that it hurt his eyes!

"What's happening?" Peter asked loudly. The light around them was much brighter than sunlight.

Jesus was standing in the middle of the clearing. But the disciples had never seen Him look like this before. His clothes were sparkling. And His face was shining. In fact, the brilliant light was coming from Jesus Himself!

"He's not alone!" James said excitedly. "There are two men with Him—Moses and the prophet Elijah.

Peter couldn't contain his excitement for one more second. He jumped up. "Teacher, it's a good thing that we three are here," Peter said. "We can build little houses here for you and Moses and Elijah."

But before Peter could finish explaining his plan, a cloud glowing with brilliant light began to fall from the sky toward the clearing. Peter backed up cautiously until he stood with John and James again. The cloud swirled and churned.

A voice like rolling thunder boomed out of the cloud, "This is my Son Jesus in whom I am well pleased. Listen to Him!"

The disciples fell on the ground and hid their faces. They were still shaking with fear when a gentle hand tapped each man on the shoulder.

"Get up and don't be afraid," said a warm, familiar voice. Peter, James, and John slowly peeked, and there was Jesus. It wasn't bright anymore, and He was alone.

"Don't tell anyone what you have seen here until I have risen from the dead," Jesus said. Then He led the disciples back to camp.

The next morning, Jesus and His disciples packed up their camp at Caesarea Philippi. They were headed south to Jerusalem for the harvest festival.

6. No Welcome in Jerusalem

Jerusalem at festival time was an exciting city.
People from all over traveled to the Jewish capital.
The narrow streets were crowded with pilgrims and
merchants. But the real center of activity was the
temple, the massive stone building that perched
royally on top of Jerusalem's highest hill. That was
the only place where Jews could offer their
sacrifices to God.

Jesus and the disciples had been in Jerusalem all
week, celebrating the harvest feast. And of course,
Jesus had been busy teaching the people in the
temple. At the edge of the crowd stood several of the

powerful Jewish leaders, who were called Pharisees.

"I don't do anything on my own," Jesus said. "But I do whatever God wants me to do. If you believe what I say and follow me, you will be free."

"But we've never been slaves," the people said. "We've always been free." The Pharisees nodded in agreement.

"If you have ever sinned, then you are a slave to sin," Jesus replied. "It controls you like a slave master. And it means that you're busy obeying your father, not my Father!"

"Our father is God," they said.

"If God were your Father, you'd love me and follow me, because I'm from God," Jesus told them. "But you don't even understand my words because your father is the devil!"

"You're crazy!" the Pharisees shouted. "You must have a demon in You to say such horrible things about us."

"I don't have a demon, but I do speak the truth," Jesus said. "I'm not trying to be important. I'm trying to show you God's glory. Whoever believes will never die."

"You don't have to say one more word!" the Pharisees yelled. "Now we're positive that a demon controls You. After all, our great father Abraham died and so did God's prophets. Do you think that You know more than they did?"

"Abraham was happy when he saw me come into the world," Jesus said.

"Abraham lived thousands of years ago," the Pharisees said. "How can You say that You've seen him?"

"Before Abraham was even born, I have always existed," Jesus answered.

"He's calling Himself God!" the Pharisees gasped. "Stop Him now!" They picked up rocks to throw at Jesus to kill Him, but Jesus slipped away into the crowd and disappeared from view. It wasn't time for Him to die—yet.

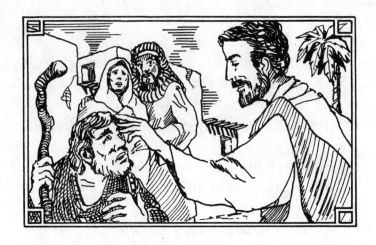

7. Light for the Blind Man

The disciples followed Jesus up the hill to the temple. It was the Sabbath, God's day of rest, and Jesus wanted to worship His Father.

As the band of men passed through the temple gate, they saw a blind man sitting on the ground. The disciples stopped Jesus and asked, "Teacher, why was this man born blind? Was it because he or his parents sinned?"

"This man's blindness wasn't caused by sin," Jesus answered. "He's blind so that God's work can be seen in him."

The blind man listened to Jesus. All his life, he had probably been told that his blindness was punishment for sin. He was thankful to hear the

28   Story based on John 9

truth and started to tell Jesus. But before he could say one word, Jesus touched him.

"I am the Light of the World," Jesus said. He spit on the ground and made some mud. He placed a little on each of the blind man's eyes. "Now go to the Pool of Siloam and wash off the mud."

The blind man didn't know what to think. But he wasn't going to argue with Jesus. He had heard that Jesus healed blind people. He hurried as quickly as he could to the Pool of Siloam.

Jesus and the disciples went on to worship.

* * * * *

The blind man made his way through the crowded streets. The Pool of Siloam was just outside the city wall. He had been there many times and knew the way by heart.

As he approached the pool, he could hear the gentle splashing of falling water. He felt the hard clay tiles beneath his feet, and stepped cautiously toward the deep pool. He edged forward until his walking stick dropped over the side of the pool. He fell to his knees and reached out. Anxiously, he splashed water on his face and rubbed the mud from his eyes.

"Oh!" he gasped. He stopped and blinked—and let out a happy shout! He could see the reflection of his own face in the still water!

He looked out across the valley and saw trees and hills and people for the first time. "I've got to thank Jesus." He threw his walking stick into the brush and retraced his steps to the temple gate.

People who saw the blind man began whispering, "That's the blind beggar, isn't it? He can see!"

"No, it's not him," someone said. "He just looks like the blind man. Whoever heard of a man born blind being able to see?"

The man heard the people talking about him. He called out to them happily, "It's me, the blind man. I can really see! Jesus did it!"

"We've got to show the Pharisees," the people said. They took the man to the Jewish leaders.

"How did you get your sight?" the Pharisees questioned. The blind man told them the story.

"This man Jesus has worked on the Sabbath!" the Pharisees shouted angrily. "How can such a sinful man be from God?"

"But if He's sinful, how could He have done this great miracle?" other Pharisees asked. "Maybe this man was not really blind. Call in his parents, and we'll get to the bottom of this!"

The man's parents were afraid. They knew the

leaders had the power to kick them out of the synagogue forever.

"Is this your son?" the Pharisees asked. "We hear he was born blind. How do you explain the fact that now he can see?"

The parents stared at the man. They couldn't believe their eyes! "He is our son, and he really was born blind. We don't have any idea how he got his sight. Ask him. He's grown up. He'll tell you."

The Pharisees were becoming frustrated. "How did you get your sight?" they bellowed.

"I already told you. Weren't you listening?" he replied bravely.

"Throw this man out of the temple forever!" the Pharisees yelled.

They tossed the man through the temple gate and told him never to come back. As he dusted himself off, a man walked up to him. "Do you believe in God's Son?" the stranger asked.

"Show me God's Son, and I'll believe," he answered.

"You are looking at Him," Jesus said.

The man bowed down before Jesus, saying, "I believe."

The Pharisees heard Jesus talking to the blind man. But they still refused to see the truth.

8. Left for Dead

Jerusalem was becoming more dangerous every day for Jesus. The Pharisees hated Him.

"It's time to leave Jerusalem for awhile," Jesus told the disciples. They all breathed a long sigh of relief. They traveled around Judea and Jesus continued to teach.

"Listen to this story," Jesus said one day.

Once there was a Jewish man who traveled down a lonely stretch of road. Suddenly a band of robbers jumped out from behind rocks, grabbed the man, and stole everything he had. And if that wasn't bad enough, they beat him until he passed out.

"Throw him into the ditch," one robber said. "Let's get out of here."

Story based on Luke 10:25-42

A Jewish priest was traveling along the road. He saw a strange pile by the roadside. "I wonder what that mess is?" he thought. "Oh! How disgusting! A dead man! I can't touch him or I'll be dirty. Wait—he moved. He's not dead, but by the looks of him he will be soon." And the priest hurried by, leaving the man in the ditch.

Pretty soon, a Levite who worked in the temple came along. He saw the beat-up man in the ditch and heard him groan painfully. "I don't want to get involved with him," the Levite thought, and he passed on by.

A little later, a Samaritan walked up the road. Samaritans and Jews hated each other. The Samaritan approached the bruised and bleeding man in the ditch. He felt so sorry for the man that he hurried over to see how he could help—even though the man was a Jew.

"This is terrible!" the Samaritan cried. He rubbed soothing ointment over the man's bruises and poured wine into his cuts. Then he put bandages on the Jewish man's wounds and wrapped him in a warm blanket and lifted him gently onto his own donkey. "I can't leave you here by the roadside," the Samaritan explained.

33

"I know of a good inn just up the road a few miles where you can stay."

The two men arrived at the inn just before sunset. The Samaritan carried the injured man into the cozy inn, and got him a bowl of steaming hot broth. He changed the man's bandages and gave him some of his own clothes to wear. The Jewish man sank into the soft bed and fell fast asleep.

The next morning the Samaritan had to continue his trip. He gave the innkeeper about $100. "Take good care of this man. I'll be back soon and I'll stop by to pay you any extra that you spend on him."

Jesus finished the story and said, "You should help others too."

* * * * *

It was getting late in the afternoon. Stomachs rumbled hungrily. Everyone agreed it was time to think about dinner.

Just around the next bend in the road was the little town of Bethany. Jesus had good friends in Bethany. And Mary, Martha and Lazarus were always glad to see Jesus. Tonight He planned to spend a quiet evening with them.

* * * * *

As He got closer and closer to the little town of Bethany, Jesus looked farther down the road and saw the towering stone wall of the temple in Jerusalem. He knew that soon He would be returning to Jerusalem for the last time.

Jesus passed by a cool grove of olive trees and walked up to a large white house. The door to the courtyard swung open. "Teacher!" Martha, the home's owner, greeted Jesus happily. "My sister Mary and I are so glad that you could share a meal with us. I only wish that my brother Lazarus could be here."

"Come and meet our other guests," Mary said, leading Jesus into the dining room. "We're anxious to hear you tell us about God."

"But first we'll have dinner," Martha said, taking Mary by the hand into the kitchen.

Mary carried the first platter of food into the room and set it on the table close to the special guest. Jesus was already talking to the people about God, and Mary stopped for a moment to listen. The next thing she knew, Martha was beside her, giving her a tug.

"Come on, Mary!" Martha scolded. "You can listen later. But right now it's more important to serve our guests. You don't want the food to be ruined, do you?"

Mary sighed, but obediently followed her sister back to the kitchen. But when she brought the next platter of food, she stopped again to listen to Jesus. His words were more refreshing than any food or water. She sat down at His feet, with the platter still in her hands.

Martha stood in the doorway trying to get Mary's attention. She wanted everything to be perfect for Jesus. She had been preparing food all day, and she was tired. If she didn't get it all served soon, it would be ruined. Was it too much to ask Mary to help serve it?

Martha interrupted Jesus saying, "Excuse me,

Teacher. Doesn't it bother You that I'm serving all of these people by myself? Please tell my sister that she should help me."

Jesus looked up into His exhausted hostess' face. He appreciated her hard work for Him. "Martha, Martha," He said lovingly. "You are so worried about everything. But really just one thing matters now. I am here with you, and Mary realizes how important that is. She has chosen to listen, and what she learns can never be taken from her."

Jesus spent the whole evening in the home of His friends teaching about God. The platters remained on the tables long after the meal was finished because now Martha was listening, too.

9. The Lost Son

A few days later, Mary and Martha, and their brother Lazarus stood on the roadside. They waved good-bye as Jesus walked away from their little town.

"Come back soon!" Martha called after Jesus. "You can stay with us whenever You're in Bethany."

It was hard to leave friends, but Jesus still had work to do. He and His disciples headed out toward the desert and crossed the Jordan River. Jesus stopped often along the way and taught people things about God's kingdom. Big crowds began to follow Jesus again. And the Pharisees were getting angrier about Him as each day passed.

"How can this teacher claim to be God's Son?" they asked each other. "He doesn't care that the people who follow Him around are sinners!"

"He seems to enjoy having those awful people close to Him," another Pharisee complained. "I couldn't stand to have them around me!"

Jesus heard them complaining, and said, "Listen, and I'll tell you a story."

Story based on Luke 15:11-32

Once there was a rich man who had two sons. One day, the younger son decided that he was tired of living at home. He wanted to be out on his own and see the world.

So the younger son went to his father. "Dad," he said, "I know that you had planned to give me half of everything you own—someday. But I don't want to wait that long. I want my half right now!"

"All right," the father said, and he gave his younger son half of everything he owned.

Now the young man was rich! He had enough money to do anything he wanted. So he decided to set out to see the world. Several days later, he started out and traveled a long way—maybe to a big city.

He had probably never seen anything like it!

There were probably huge bars that stayed open all night. The young man probably learned to drink, and probably drank a lot! He probably met lots of women dressed in flashy clothes who were glad to spend all of their time with him. They enjoyed having him spend his money on them. There may have been chariot races to bet on. And best of all, there was no one around to tell him what to do! He loved his new life.

The days flew by. He was having so much fun living wildly that he didn't even notice that he had spent all of his money. He shook the last leather bag sadly. Not one penny was left in it.

"Oh, well," he thought. "I have lots of friends in the city. They'll help me out." He probably hurried down to the bar to find the men and women who had helped him spend his fortune.

When he got there, he discovered what kind of friends those friends really were.

Maybe a woman called, "Hi! Buy me a drink!"

Maybe his friends cheered, "Yeah!"

But the young man was broke. And when his friends found out, they all walked away. The young man found out the sad truth. He *learned that friends that are bought with money leave when the money runs out.*

Perhaps the young man begged in the streets for bread, but there was a terrible shortage of food. No one would help him. After a few days he was so hungry that he decided to get a job. Finally a farmer heard him begging for a job.

"Do you care what you do to get food?" the farmer asked.

"I'll do anything!" the young man said, feeling his empty stomach rumble.

"Then I have a job for you," the farmer said.

The young man was relieved—but only for a little while. When they arrived at the farm, the young man was horrified! It was a pig farm, and Jews weren't supposed to be around pigs!

"Feed my pigs!" the farmer ordered.

"But what am I supposed to eat?" the young man asked.

"Whatever the pigs leave behind," the farmer said, laughing cruelly.

One day, as the young man threw the buckets of slop into the troughs, he came to his senses. "What am I doing here? My father's servants always have plenty to eat, and here I am

*starving to death. It's time for me to go home
and beg my father to forgive me for being such a
rotten son. I don't even deserve to be called his
son anymore. Maybe he'll let me be one of his*

servants." So the young man headed home.

*One day the father looked up and saw a man
in rags walking toward him. Something about
the man was familiar. The father squinted and
looked at him carefully.*

*"Yay!" the father yelled happily. He ran
across the field toward the man. He hugged and
kissed the young man. "Welcome home,
Son."*

*"I don't deserve to be called your son," the
young man said, ashamed.*

"Go get my best coat and put it on my son," the father ordered his servants. *"And kill the best calf for a feast to welcome him home. When he turned his back on me, he was dead to me. But he has returned and is alive!"*

The older brother was angry that his father was treating his brother so well. "I don't understand how you could have a party for the one who took your money and wasted it. You've never acted so happy to see me, and I've been here working for you and obeying you all of my life."

"Son, I'm glad that you've always been with me," the father said. *"Everything I have belongs to you. But we must celebrate your brother's return. He was lost in sin, but he has realized how bad he was. And he has turned away from that foolish life. He has come home!"*

When Jesus finished the story, the Pharisees grumbled to each other. His story just made them angrier and more determined to stop Him.

10. Too Late For Lazarus?

One bright winter morning John saw a messenger coming up the road. The servant was huffing and puffing and in a great hurry.

"There must be something wrong," John thought. "That man looks awfully worried."

"Please, Sir!" the servant called to John. "Where can I find the Teacher?"

"Follow me," John said.

Jesus saw John and the man coming. He recognized the messenger. He was a servant of Martha's and Mary's from Bethany.

"I have terrible news," the messenger said sadly. "My master, Lazarus, is very sick. His sisters thought You'd want to know because You love him."

Jesus nodded and said, "Lazarus is sick, but death won't take him yet. Lazarus' sickness will glorify God. And through his illness, God's Son will be honored."

The messenger turned to leave. What he didn't

know was that Lazarus had already died.

* * * * *

"Let's pack up," Jesus ordered the disciples. Two days had passed since the messenger from Bethany had come. "We are going back to Judea."

John and Thomas could hardly believe their ears. "But Teacher!" John protested. "Why do you want to go back there? The Pharisees want to kill you!"

"My work isn't finished yet," Jesus answered calmly. "No one will bother me now. I must go to Bethany to see our friend Lazarus. He's asleep and I have to wake him up."

"It's good that he's sleeping," John said. "That means that he's getting well."

Jesus shook His head at John. "You don't understand. Lazarus is dead."

"Oh!" the disciples gasped.

"Will you go with me now?" Jesus asked.

"We can't let Jesus go alone," Thomas said. "We must go with Him, even if that means we'll all die with Him." The disciples agreed and headed toward Bethany behind Jesus.

* * * * *

"Come quickly, Martha!" one of her friends

shouted into the house. "Jesus is coming."

Martha threw a shawl over her head and hurried to meet Jesus. Lazarus had been dead for four long days. She knew that her message to Jesus had arrived too late. But Jesus had sent such a strange answer—that Lazarus wouldn't die. What had it meant?

Martha ran up to Jesus and fell on her knees. "Master, if You'd been here I know that Lazarus would have been all right. And even now that he's dead, I know that whatever You ask God to do, He'll answer You."

Jesus touched Martha's shoulder and helped her up. "Lazarus will rise from death," Jesus said. "I am the Resurrection and the Life. Anyone who believes in me will always live with God. Do you believe that?"

"Oh, yes, Lord!" Martha answered.

"Go get your sister, Mary," Jesus told her. Martha raced back to the house to find Mary.

"Mary!" Martha called. "Jesus wants you."

Mary dashed outside and fell down at Jesus' feet. "Lord, if only You had been here my brother wouldn't have died." Tears rushed down her sad face.

Jesus was filled with sadness. "Take me to the

tomb," He said quietly. Mary and Martha led Jesus and the others to a cave surrounded by a beautiful, quiet garden. A boulder was pushed up against the cave's opening. Jesus sat down by the closed entrance of the tomb. Sad tears rolled down His face.

"Roll away the stone from the tomb's door," Jesus ordered.

"But Master, Lazarus has been dead for four days," Martha said, thinking that Jesus wanted to look at her brother. "It will stink in there."

Jesus turned to Martha. "Haven't I told you that if you believe you will see how powerful and great God is?"

"Take the stone away!" Martha told the servants. They shoved the heavy stone until the doorway was completely open.

"Father, I thank You for always listening to my prayers," Jesus said loudly, looking up toward Heaven. "I'm saying this so that the people here may know that it was You who sent me."

Jesus looked into the dark, rocky cave. "Lazarus!" He shouted. "Come out!"

Everyone held their breath. What was Jesus doing? What would happen?

Suddenly, in the doorway of the cave stood

Lazarus! He was still all tied up in sheets like a dead man—but he was alive! Everyone stared, but no one moved a muscle.

"Take those sheets off him," Jesus said.

Other people had come to the garden. "Jesus is the Son of God!" some said.

But a few crept away from the edge of the crowd. "We must report this to the Pharisees!"

The Pharisees shook their heads in disbelief, and called an emergency meeting. "This man continues to make us look like fools," they said.

"He performs many signs," one said. "Many people are following Him."

"He must be stopped immediately," they agreed. "But how?"

Caiaphas had been the high priest for many years. He was rich and powerful. "All of you act like you don't know anything," he said, as an evil look crossed his face. "Don't you realize that we must kill Jesus? We can't fool around any longer hoping that He'll disappear. We have to plan His death."

What Caiaphas and the others didn't realize was that God was in control. But the wicked men now spent all of their time plotting Jesus' death.

11. Mary's Gift

Jerusalem now held certain death for Jesus. The chief priests and the Pharisees were out to get Him. And they had spread the word throughout Jerusalem that as soon as Jesus was seen, they wanted to know where He was so they could arrest Him.

But it wasn't time for Jesus to be arrested yet. And Jesus knew that. So He took the disciples and hiked out into the wilderness to a little town called Ephraim.

There they stayed just as they had stayed many other places before. Probably the disciples were glad to be away from the city of Jerusalem and the trouble it promised.

It seems that some of the disciples had special jobs to do. Perhaps each one had assigned chores. Maybe Peter was responsible for drawing water. Maybe Andrew was responsible for the food. And it seems that Judas was responsible for the group's money. Many times faithful followers gave Jesus and the disciples gifts of money.

50 Story based on John 11:53—12:11

But Judas was not a very good treasurer. He had a habit of dipping into the funds and stealing the money. Probably nobody knew what he was doing. Nobody, that is, except Jesus!

* * * * *

One morning when the disciples awoke, they sensed something was up. They rose and dressed quickly in the brisk morning air.

"Gather around," Jesus said, and the disciples noisily encircled their leader. "We're going back to Jerusalem for the Passover feast."

"Jerusalem!" the disciples whispered to each other. "Oh, no! It's too dangerous there now!"

"I will be handed over to the Pharisees and they will sentence me to death," Jesus said. "The Romans will laugh at me, and beat me, and spit on me. I will be crucified. And three days later I will rise again."

Peter and the other disciples listened with grim faces. They were afraid, but they would follow.

* * * * *

It was a week before Passover and pilgrims from all over Palestine were arriving in the city of Jerusalem. Passover was a special festival to remember how God spared the Jews in Egypt hundreds of years before.

Now, as Passover approached, the Pharisees rubbed their hands together eagerly. "Jesus will certainly come to Jerusalem for the feast," they said. "Then we'll arrest Him!" They put out an order to all the people: "If you know where Jesus is, we order you to tell us!"

Jesus and the disciples trudged up the dusty road to Bethany. The cool garden surrounding Mary's and Martha's house was a welcome sight.

"We heard that You were on your way here, so we prepared supper for You," Martha told Jesus when she greeted Him. "Come in and eat with us."

Lazarus hugged Jesus and gave Him the place of honor at the table. Mary rushed into the room holding a small sealed pitcher. When Jesus sat down, Mary knelt beside Him and removed the cap from the pitcher.

A rich, sweet fragrance filled the room and drifted out into the courtyard and the gardens around the house. Everyone knew instantly that Mary's pitcher contained the most expensive perfume in the world. And the pitcher was full!

Mary had treasured the pitcher of perfume for many years, and had saved it for the most special moment of her life. She knew that the moment had finally come. She bent down and poured all of the perfume on Jesus' tired, dusty feet. And then, without a moment's hesitation, she uncovered her long, thick hair and used it like a towel to wipe His feet dry. No one said a word, but everyone was overcome with her love for Jesus. Except one person.

"That's an awful waste!" a voice broke the silence. It was Judas Iscariot. "That perfume was worth hundreds of dollars. Why wasn't it sold and the money given to the poor?" Judas touched the leather money bag inside his cloak. He liked to feel the coins and listen to them jingle. And he liked to steal them for himself. If the perfume had been sold, there would have been more coins for Judas to secretly take.

"Don't scold Mary," Jesus ordered. "There will always be poor people for you to serve, but you won't always have me with you."

From that time on, Judas clutched the money bag more tightly than ever before. Soon he would get his chance to be rich—at Jesus' expense!

12. Welcoming the King

Jesus stopped near the Mount of Olives. He called two of the disciples to Him.

"I want you to go up into that village. You'll find the colt of a donkey tied up there. It's never been ridden by anyone before. Bring it to me."

"But what if someone sees us taking it?" the men said, worriedly.

"Tell them that the Lord needs it," Jesus replied.

The disciples hurried away and found the colt, just as Jesus had described.

"Hey!" a man called to them. "Just where do you think you're taking that colt?"

"The Lord needs it," the disciples answered, and no one stopped them. They led the young donkey back to the Mount of Olives where Jesus was.

"It happened just like You said it would," they told Jesus happily. They all spread their cloaks across the colt's back.

As Jesus swung His leg over the colt, Peter closed

Story based on Mark 11:1-10 and 14:10,11

55

his eyes. The colt had never been ridden and he was sure it would go wild with a person on its back. But the only sound he heard was a contented whinny from the colt. Peter opened his eyes, and to his surprise, the colt seemed happy to carry Jesus!

Perhaps John whispered to Peter, "Jesus is doing what the old Scriptures said He would. Remember in the book of Zechariah? The prophet said that the King would come riding on a colt!"

The disciples were becoming more excited by the minute. Jesus would enter Jerusalem as the long-awaited King of Israel!

Jesus gave the little colt a gentle nudge and the animal trotted down the road toward the gates of Jerusalem. The disciples followed.

"Jesus is coming! The Teacher is coming for Passover!" Word spread quickly as the men approached the city. Everyone knew the danger Jesus faced, and that made the people admire Him even more!

By the time Jesus arrived at the city gates, hundreds of people lined the road hoping to see the King. Many people spread their cloaks and shawls on the road so that the colt wouldn't kick up any dust on Jesus. Others cut long palm branches and set them across the road.

"Hosanna! Hosanna to the promised King!" the people shouted. They were hoping that Jesus would at last save them from the Romans.

The Pharisees came running to see what was going on. They got there just in time to see Jesus ride through the city gates.

"He's headed for the temple," they said to each other with alarm. All of Jerusalem was alive with shouting and cheering for Jesus. The Jewish leaders stood around the edges of the excited crowd. "How dare He march in here and take over!" they complained bitterly to each other. "It's worse than we thought it'd be. The people are calling Him the King!"

Caiaphas gathered the leaders in the council room. "We must kill Jesus now before any more people believe," he said.

"But how?" they asked. "We must arrest Him secretly, but we don't know where He goes when He leaves Jerusalem."

"We need some inside help," Caiaphas said. "Someone who knows Him well."

"But who can we get?" the other leaders asked.

Just then, a priest came running into the council room, saying breathlessly, "One of Jesus' disciples is here! He wants to talk with us privately."

"Bring him to us immediately!" Caiaphas ordered.

The door opened and in walked Judas Iscariot. He had gladly become a disciple when he heard that Jesus was going to be the King. When Jesus took the throne, Judas knew that he would become rich and powerful. But he was tired of waiting. He wanted to be rich now—not sometime in the far-off future.

"How much will you pay me to lead you to Jesus?" Judas asked, rubbing his hands together greedily.

The Pharisees and priests smiled wickedly. What good luck they were having today!

"How about thirty silver coins?" Caiaphas offered. "That's a lot of money."

"All right!" Judas agreed, and took the coins. "I'll have to find the best time to take you to Him."

"Yes," said Caiaphas. "We want it to be a secret from the people."

Judas grinned, and sneaked back to the place where Jesus and the disciples were staying. He felt the silver coins in the bag. Finally, he was a rich man.

13. The Bread and the Cup

Peter and John struggled through the crowded streets of Jerusalem. The city was packed with Jewish pilgrims from all over the world. There were merchants lining every street selling their wares—everything from fine silks to exotic spices.

Can you imagine Peter passing all those food merchants? Especially the little meat pies. They smelled soooo good!

"Just a nickel," a merchant may have called, temptingly.

But they didn't have time to eat. They had work to do. Important work. Work for Jesus. They needed to keep looking for a man with a pitcher.

There were lots of women with pitchers. That was normal. Women usually were the ones to go to the well and get water. But it would not be so easy to find a man with a pitcher.

Story based on Luke 22:1-20 and John 14:1-12

But Jesus had said there would be one, so Peter and John knew that sooner or later they would surely run into one.

"Look!" John said, pointing. In the midst of the women there was one man filling a very large pitcher. "That's him! Come on, Peter." The two disciples trailed the man through the crowded streets to a narrow alley.

"He went into the second door on the right," Peter said. "This must be the place." John knocked on the door, and when the owner answered, Peter said, "Jesus sent us to ask you to show us the room where He will spend the Passover."

"I've been waiting for you," the owner of the house answered. "Right this way." He led Peter and John up the stairs to a large, comfortable room that was set up for the Passover meal.

"Thank you," the disciples said to the owner. "All we have to do now is get the food and meet Jesus."

* * * * *

Jesus arrived at the house with His disciples early in the evening. Jerusalem had grown quiet as everyone prepared the special Passover meal. The streets were nearly empty.

After the disciples had settled down in the large room, Jesus took off His robes and wrapped a towel around His waist. He poured water into a large bowl and set it on the floor near the disciples.

"What's He doing?" the disciples whispered. Jesus knelt before one of the disciples and began to wash his feet. "Only servants wash people's feet!" the shocked disciples said. But Jesus moved quietly from one man to the next, dipping their dusty feet into the bowl and then drying them with the towel He was wrapped in.

Peter watched as Jesus knelt before each man. When it was his turn, Peter looked at his Master and said, "Lord, I can't let You wash my feet!"

"If you won't let me wash your feet, you aren't my disciple," Jesus answered.

Peter quickly put his feet into the water, and said, "If washing my feet makes me Your follower, Lord, then wash my head and hands, too! I am totally Yours."

"You don't need your head and hands washed, Peter," Jesus said to him. "You are clean already. But there is one man here who is dirty." Judas Iscariot squirmed a little wondering if Jesus knew what he had done.

When Jesus had finished, He put His robe on

and sat with the twelve men. "Do you know why I washed your feet? I am your Master and Lord, but I acted like your servant. I want you to act the same way. Serve each other."

During the Passover meal, Jesus looked around at His disciples sadly. "One of you is going to go against me," He said.

"Oh, no!" the men cried. "Who? Me?" they all asked.

Even Judas Iscariot asked, "Is it me?"

"You said it," Jesus answered him quietly. "Do what you have to do quickly."

Judas leaped up from the table and hurried out of the room. Because he kept the money, everyone thought he was leaving to buy something else for their feast. But Jesus knew that when Judas returned he wouldn't be alone.

Jesus watched the door close and then turned to the remaining eleven disciples. Tonight none of you will stay beside me."

Peter couldn't believe his ears. How could any of them turn away from Jesus? "I'll never leave You!" he said.

"Before you hear the rooster crow at dawn, Peter, you will have said three times that you don't know me," Jesus said.

"Never! Even if I must die beside You, I'll never say that I don't know You!" Peter vowed. And all of the other disciples agreed.

Jesus knew that the disciples meant to stick by Him. But none of them knew how difficult the night would be.

When the meal was finished, Jesus took a piece of the flat, cracker-like bread. He prayed, giving thanks for it to God. He broke off pieces of the bread and gave a little to each man. No one had ever eaten after the Passover meal before. Jesus was doing something new. The disciples didn't know it yet, but Jesus was telling them that the Passover meal was finished forever. He Himself was the Lamb whose blood would save the people from death for all time.

"Eat this piece of bread," Jesus ordered. "This is my body which is given for you." Quietly, the disciples obeyed.

Then Jesus took a cup of wine and thanked God for it. "Drink this. It is my blood which is my promise to erase all of the sins of the people who believe. Do this often and remember me until I come again."

The disciples were worried. What did all of this mean? Where was Jesus going?

"Don't worry," Jesus said, seeing their concerned faces. "Believe in God and in me, too. I'm leaving to get a place ready for you. You'll be there with me always. You know how to get there."

"But Lord, if we don't know where You're going, how can we know how to get there?" Thomas asked.

"I am the Way and the Truth and the Life," Jesus answered. "There's no other way to get to the Father. You must come to Him by me. If you know me, you know my Father."

Philip was confused by all of this. "We'll understand if you show us the Father," he said.

Jesus shook His head at Philip. "You've been with me all of this time and still don't know who I am? Everyone who has seen me has also seen the Father. I'm leaving you, but you won't be alone. The Father will send the Holy Spirit to live in each of you. If you love me, you will follow my orders. But now, in the hours ahead, don't be afraid. Know that I have already won the battle."

The disciples listened carefully. They knew without a doubt that Jesus had come from God. But not one of them was ready for what would happen next.

14. In the Garden

The streets of Jerusalem were dark, but Jesus and the eleven disciples could hear happy voices in the houses they passed. At midnight the temple gates would open, and the celebrating people would once again flood the streets and head to the temple.

Jesus was leading the disciples away from the temple to the Kidron Brook. The full moon shone like daylight. On the other side of the spring-swollen river, the disciples followed Jesus into a small garden called Gethsemane. They had spent many hours before with Jesus among the fruit trees

Story based on Luke 22:39-62 and John 18:1-18

and shrubs of this garden. It was one of the Teacher's favorite places.

"Sit down here by the garden's gate," Jesus said to the disciples. "I'm going into the garden to pray. Peter, James, and John will come with me."

The other eight disciples settled down on the grass by the gate. The day had been long and tiring, and soon they were all asleep.

Jesus walked a little way into the garden, then turned to the three He had taken with Him. In the moonlight, Peter could see that the Teacher's face was full of sorrow.

"I am so sad," Jesus said to them. "Sad enough to die. Stay awake with me and pray."

Peter, James, and John sat on the grass and watched Jesus walk further into the garden. He fell to the ground, face first, and began to pray. "My Father, if it's possible, please stop this terrible thing that's about to happen to me. But whatever You want me to do, I will." Huge drops of blood and sweat dripped from His forehead.

After a little while, Jesus returned and found the three men lying on the grass fast asleep.

"Peter!" Jesus called. "Couldn't you stay awake with me for an hour? Wake up now and pray that you won't do anything you'll be sorry for."

Peter shook his head sleepily. He sat up again and watched as Jesus began to pray a second time. But no matter how hard he tried, Peter just couldn't keep his eyes open.

"My Father," Jesus prayed, "if I must do this thing, I will." He returned to the three men. And again, they were all asleep.

Jesus prayed for the third time, saying the same thing. But now He was filled with God's power because He was obedient to His Father's will. The sorrow and struggling were gone. Jesus knew He would win the battle with death.

He stood by the sleeping disciples. "Rest now," He said softly. "Judas Iscariot will be here soon."

* * * * *

The disciples awoke with a jolt. Soldiers were coming!

Peter heard the thunder of many feet approaching quickly. In spite of the bright moonlight, the soldiers carried torches as if they were searching for a thief. Peter looked toward the gate and saw Judas Iscariot run through it into the garden. Roman soldiers and temple guards were on his heels. They had their swords drawn!

"Teacher!" Judas shouted as he kissed Jesus.

That was the sign the soldiers and guards were supposed to watch for.

"So, Judas, you turn me over to these people with a kiss," Jesus said softly. Judas stepped back into the band of soldiers.

"Who are you looking for?" Jesus asked them.

"Jesus of Nazareth," the temple guards answered.

"I am Jesus." He spoke with such power that the soldiers and guards fell down backwards! "If you're only looking for me, let these other men go."

The soldiers stepped forward and grabbed Jesus.

Peter wondered if he should attack. But he didn't wait for instructions. He pulled out his sword and swung it at the high priest's servant. Whoosh! Peter's aim was off and instead of hitting the man squarely on the head, the sword slipped and sliced off the man's right ear.

"Stop, now!" Jesus commanded. "Put your sword away. My Father has given me something I must do." Gently, He reached out and touched the servant's ear. It was healed instantly.

The temple guards quickly tied up Jesus. "Don't let Him get away!" they warned the soldiers. Then

Jesus was dragged away like a criminal. The disciples shook with fear. Probably each one was thinking the very same thing: that he would be arrested next. So they all ran away, leaving Jesus alone with the guards.

* * * * *

John and Peter hid in the garden's shrubs for a few minutes. They watched the band of soldiers and guards disappear with Jesus up the trail toward Jerusalem.

"Let's follow them," Peter said, and the two disciples ran up the path. They reached the soldiers just in time to see Jesus brought to the courtyard of the high priest, Caiaphas.

"Wait here," John told Peter. "I know the high priest. I'm sure the girl at the gate will let us into the courtyard."

Peter watched as John talked with the servant at the gate. After a moment, he waved to Peter. "Come on!" he said, and the two men slipped through the gate.

"I'm going to try to find out what's happening to Jesus," John whispered. "Stay here in the courtyard. I'll be back soon."

Peter stood by the gate nervously. He knew if he made any false moves he would be arrested, too.

The woman servant at the gate studied his face. He looked away from her. "Aren't you one of Jesus' disciples?" she asked.

"No, I'm not," he answered quickly. He walked away from her toward the middle of the courtyard. It was a chilly night, and the temple guards had built a fire to keep warm.

Peter moved closer to the fire. The warmth felt good. He held his hands out and rubbed them together. Then he noticed that the guards were staring at him. He looked down at the ground.

"You're a disciple of the prisoner's, aren't you?" one of the guards asked, trying to get a better look at Peter's face.

"I don't even know Him!" Peter protested as he left the bright fire. He couldn't risk being recognized. He wandered around the crowded courtyard, wishing that John would come back so they could leave.

"Open the gates!" the temple guards called. "The leaders are coming now to put Jesus on trial for lying about God!" Peter watched from the shadows as several of the priests and Pharisees hurried through the gate and into Caiaphas' house.

Peter crept closer to the guards to hear their conversation. Maybe he'd learn what was going to happen to Jesus.

Suddenly, one of the guards glanced over and spotted Peter. "Hey," he hollered. "Weren't you with Jesus in the garden tonight? Yeah, sure you were. You were the one with the sword!"

"I don't know anything about Jesus!" Peter swore.

Just then a rooster crowed to greet the new morning. Jesus' words came flooding back into Peter's memory.

Jesus was right. Peter had turned his back on the Lord three times.

Peter pushed through the crowd to the gate. He ran out of the courtyard, and down the streets of Jerusalem, crying bitterly.

15. On Trial

Pontius Pilate didn't like these sticky Jewish affairs. He had been the Roman governor of Judea for seven years and he still wasn't sure how to handle the Jews. Usually the Jewish leaders wanted to settle their own problems, and Pilate had learned the hard way that it was best to let them do whatever they wanted to. But today, the Jewish leaders were begging him to solve one of their problems. They wanted him to kill a man.

"This man is not guilty of anything," Pilate told the leaders as he pointed at Jesus. "I can't find any fault in Him."

"Our trial found Him guilty!" Caiaphas exclaimed. "Jesus has been going all over Judea trying to get the people to riot!"

Pilate tapped his chin thoughtfully. There was more to this situation than met the eye. The priests and Pharisees were jealous of Jesus. And they were doing all they could to get rid of Him.

"Let me make a suggestion," Pilate said, trying to calm Caiaphas. "I'll order my soldiers to beat Him. That should make Him think twice about disobeying you in the future. Then we can release Him."

"Beating Him is not enough," Caiaphas argued. "That won't stop Him. He deserves to die."

"No, He doesn't!" Pilate said again. "I let one prisoner go during Passover each year. I'll let the people decide who it will be this year—Jesus or somebody else."

Caiaphas smiled wickedly. All day the priests had been wandering through the crowded streets spreading lies about Jesus. "Jesus is dangerous!" they had whispered. "He says that He is the King. What will the emperor Caesar do when he hears that? He'll send thousands of his best soldiers against us and destroy us!"

"Oh, no!" the people cried, believing the lies. They were quick to turn against Jesus. "How can we stop Him?"

"He must be killed!" the priests said. "That's the only answer."

The courtyard outside the Judgment Hall quickly filled with an angry mob. Pilate stood on a balcony and raised his arms to try to get their attention.

"I will release a prisoner to you today," he shouted. "Who do you want—Barabbas the murderer, or Jesus?"

"Give us Barabbas!" the mob yelled.

"But what should I do with Jesus who is called your King?" Pilate asked.

"Crucify Him!" they all shouted.

"He hasn't done anything to deserve death," Pilate said.

"Crucify Him! Crucify Him!" the mob chanted wildly, waving their fists in the air. "He must die for calling Himself the Son of God!"

A sweat broke out on Pilate's forehead. He turned to Jesus. "Who are You?" he asked. But Jesus was silent. "Speak to me!" Pilate demanded. "Don't you know that I have the power to kill You or to set You free?"

"You have no power over me at all," Jesus answered calmly. "The only power you have is the power that God gives you."

Pilate felt his knees knocking with fear. He knew that he didn't want to be responsible for this man's death. But he was even more afraid of the fury of the mob. He led Jesus out to the people. "Look at your King!" he yelled. He hoped they would change their minds.

But the people screamed loudly, "Take Him away! Crucify Him!"

"You want me to kill your King?" Pilate cried out.

"Caesar is our only King!" the priests yelled.

The mob boiled in the courtyard, screaming and leaping at Jesus. "I can't stand up against this crowd," Pilate thought. "There'll be a riot if I don't do what they're demanding." He ordered a bowl of water to be brought to him.

"Look!" Pilate yelled at the mob. He splashed his hands in the water. "I'm washing the blood of this innocent man from my hands. I'm not responsible for His death! You are the guilty ones!"

"We're guilty!" they shouted back. "We're glad to be responsible for His death!"

Pilate stumbled back into the palace. He didn't have the courage to look at Jesus. "Guards! Let Barabbas go. Then take this man, beat Him, and crucify Him!"

* * * * *

Word spread quickly throughout Jerusalem. "Jesus will be crucified! He is condemned to death for lying about being God!" Everyone heard the news, including Judas Iscariot. He reached into his coat and pulled out the leather bag filled with the silver coins. He ran to the temple to return the coins to the priests. "I sold an innocent man to you!" he cried. "I did a terrible thing."

"That's not our problem," they told him.

"I don't want your money!" Judas said and threw the coins. They clattered noisily against the stone floor. He turned and ran out of the temple, through the city gate, and away from the awful crowds that were shouting, "Crucify Him!"

Judas ran far into the fields, but still he could hear the people shouting. He covered his ears, but their voices rang in his head. There was only one way to escape his crime. He threw a rope over a tree and hanged himself.

Back in Jerusalem the mob anxiously waited for Jesus to be brought out to them. "Crucify Him! Crucify Him!" they chanted.

16. The Cross

John pushed through the angry crowd. He could see Jesus stumbling along the street, carrying a massive cross-beam on his sagging shoulders. His robe was dirty and stained with blood from the beating the soldiers had given Him. And on His head there was a crown made of thorns, pricking His forehead.

Hot tears stung John's eyes. He watched helplessly as Jesus passed by. Suddenly Jesus fell to His knees under the weight of the beam. John could see that Jesus was exhausted from the cruel beating.

"You!" a soldier yelled, grabbing a man from the crowd. "Carry the prisoner's beam!" The man whose name was Simon was afraid to say no, so he lifted the beam off Jesus' back. The soldier dragged Jesus to His feet. "Get moving!" he shouted and the

78   Story based on Matthew 27:32-50 and John 19:16-30

gruesome parade started again.

John joined the crowd. He followed the soldiers and their three prisoners to a hill outside the city that looked like a skull. The hill was called Golgotha.

The sound of hammers striking nails echoed across the rocks. By the time John reached Golgotha, the Romans had already set up the three posts upon which Jesus and two thieves would be crucified.

John's stomach turned as he watched one of the soldiers drive long nails through Jesus' wrists into the wooden cross-beam. They hoisted the cross-beam into place, and tied it to the upright post. With another sickening thud, a nail was hammered through Jesus' feet into the post. Blood trickled from the wounds, but Jesus never said a word.

"That's a nice looking tunic," a greedy soldier said, inspecting Jesus' robe. "Let's cast lots for it."

"Before we divide up the loot, let's finish our work," the head soldier ordered. "We still need to nail up the sign that Pilate gave us. It goes over the head of this prisoner," he said, pointing to Jesus.

One of the soldiers read the sign loudly: "This is

Jesus, the King of the Jews." All of the soldiers laughed. And so did the chief priests and the Pharisees. They had come to make sure Jesus didn't escape this time.

"You said that You could save people," the priests jeered. "What's wrong with You now? Can't You save Yourself?"

"If You really were sent by God to be our King, why don't You prove it by coming down off of the cross? Then we'll believe!" the Pharisees said with sneers on their smug faces. Jesus didn't pay any attention to them.

John crept up to the hilltop and stood at the base of the cross. He looked up into Jesus' face and heard his Lord's labored breathing. Death on the cross was one of the longest, most painful ways a person could die. And most people hung for days before dying.

Jesus' tired eyes gazed at His friend John. The disciple could see the dreadful pain that Jesus was suffering. John felt helpless and hopeless as he stood before Jesus' limp, hanging body.

A group of weeping women approached the cross. It was Jesus' earthly mother Mary, her sister and Mary Magdalene. They were devoted followers of Jesus.

"Woman," Jesus spoke to Mary gently. She looked up into His face. "John will be your son now." Then Jesus looked at John. "Treat this woman as your own mother." John put his arm around Mary's shoulders to comfort her.

Suddenly the daylight faded, and a strange darkness spread across the land. Jesus groaned and cried out in pain. He was the sacrificed Lamb whose blood would cover the sins of everyone who believed in Him.

After three long hours of terrible suffering, Jesus stopped groaning and said in a strong voice, "My work is finished." John saw Jesus bow His head. He took one more earthly breath and then sent His spirit out of His body. The earth shook and the Roman soldiers fell to the ground in fear. Jesus was dead.

17. Alive!

"We've come for Jesus' body," Joseph of Arimathea told the soldiers. "We have Pilate's permission to bury Him before sunset." The soldiers stared at the two wealthy men. They were not like Jesus' other followers. They were members of the Jewish council!

Joseph and Nicodemus gently eased the nails from the wrists and feet of their Lord. Tears ran down their faces. They had not been invited to Jesus' secret midnight trial at Caiaphas' house. And they hadn't had any part in demanding His death. But because they were afraid of the other Jewish leaders, they had never openly admitted that they were His followers.

The two leaders wound clean cloth and spices around Jesus' body. They had loved this man, and for the first time neither of them cared who saw them with Him. They carried Jesus' body to a nearby cave where no one had ever been buried, and placed Him gently on the rocky floor.

Nicodemus and Joseph ordered their servants to push a large, heavy boulder into the cave's opening

Story based on Matthew 26:61—28:9 and John 19:38—20:18

to keep Jesus' body safe from animals. Then, sadly, they went home.

Meanwhile, the Pharisees were at it again. They were plotting up a storm. They too were worried that something might happen to Jesus' body. And they weren't worried about animals as Nicodemus and Joseph had been. They were afraid that if Jesus' body disappeared from the grave, the disciples—and everyone else who heard about it—would believe that Jesus really was the Son of God! And they sure couldn't let that happen!

"Jesus said that He would rise up in three days," they told Pilate worriedly. "We must seal the tomb and have soldiers guard it day and night, or His followers might steal the body. Then they'd tell everyone that He had risen."

Pilate agreed and sent soldiers to stand by the cave. The leaders sealed the stone with mud so that no one could get in!

* * * * *

Just before dawn, the air was still and quiet in the garden around the cave where Jesus' body had been laid. The soldiers stood guard in front of the boulder-blocked entrance. It had been three days since Joseph and Nicodemus had placed Jesus' body there.

Just then a mighty earthquake thundered through the rocks! And the stone rolled away from the entrance to the cave.

Brilliant light flooded the dark garden and in the light stood an angel from God!

* * * * *

It was early in the morning. The sun had risen over the Judean hillsides with all its usual splendor. Already, many Jews were busy about their daily tasks, hoping to beat the midday heat.

Mary Magdalene filled a small wicker basket with burial spices. Soon she and two other women were heading down the pathway to the place where Jesus' body had been laid.

Mary knew it might not be easy, but she was bound and determined to annoint Jesus' body one last time. "There's a huge stone in the door of the cave," she told her companions. "I don't know how we'll ever move it by ourselves."

But to their surprise, the stone was already rolled away. And the Roman soldiers were gone!

Mary looked at her friends with alarm. Something was wrong. She ran across the garden and looked into the cave.

"Jesus' body is gone!" she called to the women. Tears streamed down her face. Without a moment to lose, she raced out of the garden and went to find Peter and John. They would know what to do.

"What's wrong?" Peter asked her as she bolted into the house.

"Someone has stolen Jesus' body!" Mary cried breathlessly. "We can't find it!"

Without another word, Peter and John ran out of the house. John reached the cave first and looked inside. The cloth that Jesus had been wrapped in was still wound up neatly as if it contained a body—but it didn't!

"What's happened?" Peter asked, crawling into the tomb to get a better look. He could plainly see that Jesus had vanished. "The burial cloth hasn't been taken apart. Jesus' body couldn't have been taken by anyone."

"He has risen from death," John thought. "It's the third day. Jesus must be alive!"

John and Peter walked home slowly, thinking about the mysterious disappearance.

Mary was on her way back to the cave. She just missed the two disciples. She walked into the garden, sobbing her heart out. "If only I could see Jesus' body again," she thought. Hopefully, she leaned down and looked into the cave.

"Oh!" she gasped. Two angels were sitting by

Jesus' burial cloth.

"Why are you crying so hard?" the angels asked her.

"Someone has taken my Lord's body and I don't know where it is," she cried. Her eyes were flooded with tears. She turned back toward the garden and saw a man standing there.

"Why are you crying?" the man asked. "Who are you looking for?"

Mary looked at the man through her tears and thought it was the gardener. "Did you take my Lord's body out of this tomb?" she asked. "If you did, please show me where it is."

"Mary," Jesus said to her gently. Quickly she rubbed the tears from her eyes and saw that the man was Jesus Himself.

"Teacher!" she said. She fell at His feet and clutched His ankles.

"Don't hold onto me," He said, "but go to the others and tell them that I am alive and will soon be going to be with my Father."

Jesus visited the disciples Himself many times in the weeks that followed His resurrection. He ate with them and talked with them, and even let them touch the wounds on His hands where the nails had been.

The Pharisees were furious that Jesus' body had disappeared. They didn't waste any time spreading rumors that the disciples had stolen the body. But Jesus' followers knew better. They all rejoiced that Jesus was alive!

18. Peter Goes Fishing

Now that Jesus had risen from the dead, He didn't stay with His disciples like He used to. They were never sure where or when He would come.

It had been a long time since the disciples had seen Jesus. He had told them He would meet them at the Sea of Galilee. But He hadn't said when. Just like He hadn't said when He would become King. It was hard to just sit around and wait.

Peter paced up and down the beach. He skipped stones across the blue sea waves for awhile. And then he got an idea. "I'm going fishing!" he told the other disciples.

Story based on John 21

"That's better than doing nothing," they agreed. "We'll go with you." They hopped into a boat and rowed out onto the lake.

"Throw the nets out!" Peter ordered. They fished all night. But they didn't catch one fish!

As the sun was rising, Jesus appeared on the beach. He could see the fishing boat bobbing on the water. "Hey!" He shouted. "Have you caught anything?" The disciples didn't recognize Him.

"Not even one little fish!" Peter shouted back.

"Throw your nets over the right-hand side of the boat," Jesus said. And as soon as they did, the nets were so full the disciples couldn't haul them in.

"It's Jesus!" John said to Peter.

Peter let out a joyful shout and jumped into the lake. He swam with long, powerful strokes toward the shore. The other disciples rowed the boat back, dragging the heavy nets.

On the beach, they discovered a cheery fire burning, with fish already cooking on the coals.

"Bring your fish, too," Jesus said. They pulled in the bulging nets and counted over 150 fish! And the nets weren't even torn from the weight.

"Come and eat breakfast," Jesus said, sitting beside Peter. "Peter, do you love me with a perfect love?"

Peter thought for a few minutes before he answered. With shame in his voice, Peter said, "You know that I love You like a brother."

"Watch out for my lambs, and feed them," Jesus said. They were quiet for a few minutes, and then Jesus asked a second time, "Peter, do you love me with a perfect love?"

Peter sighed and felt miserable. He knew that he had let Jesus down. "I love You like a brother," he answered again.

"Care for my sheep," Jesus instructed him.

Peter poked a stick at the dying coals of the fire. Jesus was giving him a job to do, and he wanted to serve Jesus more than anything in the world. But would he do a good job? He had let Jesus down and he couldn't brag anymore about being the most devoted disciple. Being honest hurt.

"Peter," Jesus said gently, "do you really love me like a brother?"

Tears welled up in Peter's eyes. Was Jesus even doubting his affection? "Lord, You know everything," Peter said. "I can't hide anything from You. You know that I really do love You like a brother."

Jesus nodded. "Take care of my sheep," He said. "And follow me!"

Peter obeyed Jesus' instructions. Forty days after Jesus left the tomb alive, Peter watched Him rise from the earth into Heaven to sit at the Father's right hand. And Peter fearlessly loved and served His King for the rest of his life.